This book belongs to …

The Magic Button and Other Stories

How this collection works

This *Read with Biff, Chip & Kipper* collection is the fourth in the series at Level 2. It is divided into two distinct halves.

The first half focuses on phonics-based reading practice. It contains eight amusing *Talk-about Situations* and a story called *The Magic Button.* The second half contains two separate *Stories for Wider Reading* that use everyday language. These stories help to broaden your child's wider reading experience. There are fun activities to enjoy throughout the book.

How to use this book

Find a time to read with your child when they are not too tired and are happy to concentrate for about ten to fifteen minutes. Reading at this stage should be a shared and enjoyable experience. It is best to choose just the *Talk-about Situations* or one of the stories for each session.

There are tips for reading together for each part of the book. The first tips are on pages 6 and 28. They show you how to introduce your child to the phonics stories. Tips to tell you how you can best approach reading the stories with a wider vocabulary are given on page 50.

Enjoy sharing the stories!

The **Helping Your Child to Read** handbook contains a wealth of practical information, tips and activities.

OXFORD

UNIVERSITY PRESS

Oxford University Press is a department of the University of Oxford.
It furthers the University's objective of excellence in research, scholarship,
and education by publishing worldwide. Oxford is a registered trade mark
of Oxford University Press in the UK and in certain other countries

Talk-about Situations, The Magic Button text © Roderick Hunt and Annemarie Young 2016
Creepy-crawly!, The Lost Puppy text © Roderick Hunt 1995, 1996
Talk-about Situations, The Magic Button illustrations © Alex Brychta 2016
Creepy-crawly!, The Lost Puppy illustrations © Alex Brychta 1995, 1996

The characters in this work are the original creation of Roderick Hunt
and Alex Brychta who retain copyright in the characters.

The moral rights of the authors have been asserted

Talk-about Situations, The Magic Button first published in 2016
Creepy-crawly! first published in 1995
The Lost Puppy first published in 1996

ISBN: 978-0-19-276381-5

1

Paper used in the production of this book is a natural, recyclable product made
from wood grown in sustainable forests. The manufacturing process conforms
to the environmental regulations of the country of origin.

Printed in China

Acknowledgements

Series Editor: Annemarie Young

The Magic Button

and Other Stories

OXFORD
UNIVERSITY PRESS

Tips for the Talk-about Situations

These eight amusing situations are designed to motivate your child to predict what might happen next.

- Tell your child they are going to look at a series of pictures where something is about to happen.
- Talk about what is in the picture. Ask your child what is happening and what they think is going to happen next. Ask them to read any sound effect words in the picture, for example 'Fizz!'
- When you turn the page to see what actually happens, the outcome may or may not be what you expect! Talk about it.
- Ask your child to read the sound effect words in the picture (for example, 'Pop!'), and to read the simple sentence under the picture. All of the words on the outcome pages are phonically decodable.

Have fun!

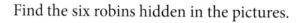
Find the six robins hidden in the pictures.

The talk-about situations practise these letter sounds:
j w x y zz ll ff ss ch ck ng qu

For more hints and tips on helping your child become a successful and enthusiastic reader look at our website www.oxfordowl.co.uk.

Talk-about Situations

Let's have some fun.

Talk about each picture.

Guess what's going to happen next!

What is Kipper doing?
What is Mum saying?
What will happen next?

9

Kipper got wet!

What is Kipper doing? Why?
What will happen next?

It fell in the jug!

What are Dad and Biff doing?
What will happen next?

Dad had a miss.

What has Wilma found?
What will she do next?

Wilma put the duckling back.

What is the clown doing?
What will happen next?

17

Puff! Hiss! Fizz! Pop! Bang!

What is making that sound?

Lick! Lick!

Yum, yum!

What are the children waiting for?

The man rang the bell.

What is Gran doing?
What will happen next?

Gran fell into the box!

Matching

Match the sound words to the pictures.

Quack! Quack!

Ping! Pong!

Chuff chug!

Yuck!

Bang!

Ding dong!

Maze

Help the train get to the children.

Read these sentences again

Kipper got wet!

Puff! Hiss! Fizz! Pop! Bang!

It fell in the jug!

Lick! Lick! Yum, yum!

Dad had a miss.

The man rang the bell.

Wilma put the duckling back.

Gran fell into the box!

- Talk about the title and the picture on the opposite page.
- Look at the words on page 30. Say the sounds in each word and then say the word (e.g. *g-o-b-l-i-n, goblin; b-u-tt-o-n, button*).
- The story uses the words *I, the, is, said* and *do*. These are 'tricky' words that can't be sounded out, but they are useful common words. When you come to them in the story, read them to your child.
- Read the story with your child, placing your finger under each word as you read together.
- Read the story again and encourage your child to do most of the reading.
- Give lots of praise as your child reads with you.
- Do the fun activities at the end of the story.

Children enjoy re-reading stories and this helps to build their confidence.

Have fun!

 After you have read the story, find the ten cotton reels hidden in the pictures.

The main sounds practised in this story are 'j' as in *jug*, 'x' as in *wax* and *box*, 'z' as in *fizz*, 'ck' as in *back* and *packet*, 'ng' as in *zing* and *bong*, 'qu' as in *liquid*, and 'th' as in *thin* and *thud*

 For more hints and tips on helping your child become a successful and enthusiastic reader look at our website www.oxfordowl.co.uk.

The Magic Button

Read these words.

liquid	jug
wax	fizz
thud	zing
bong	bing
back	packet

A button fell off Chip's top.

The button fell into the bin.

"I can get it back on,"
said Chip.

Chip got into a mess.

"Let me do it," said Gran.

Chip had a nap.

A big goblin had a tin jug.

"Put in liquid wax," said
the big goblin.

Hiss, fizz, pop!

"Put in a packet of pins," said
a thin goblin.

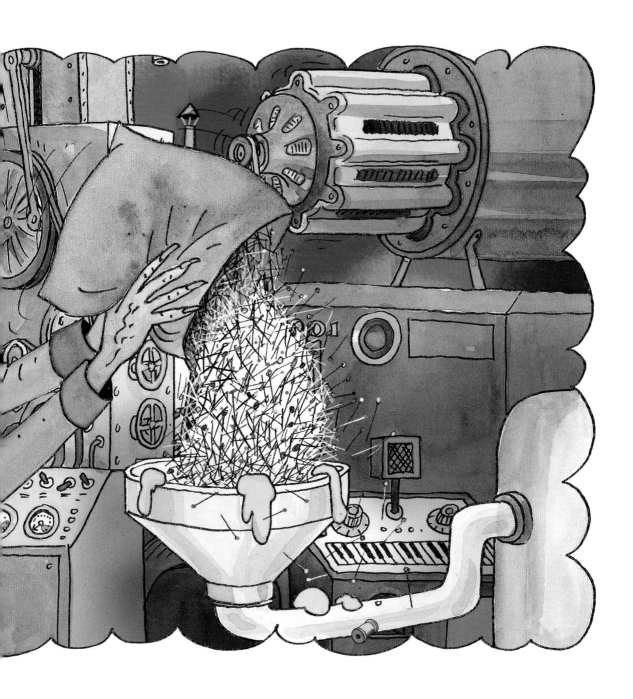

Hum, thud, hum, thud!

"Tip in a box of bits," said

a red goblin.

Zip, zing, bing, bong!

"This is it," said the red goblin.

"A button!"

"It is a magic button," said
the big goblin.

"Magic, Gran!" said Chip.

What did the goblins put in?

Read the words and match the pictures to complete the phrase.

a packet of

liquid wax

a jug of

bits

a box of

pins

Maze

Help Chip make the magic button.

Stories for Wider Reading

Tips for Reading Together

These two stories use simple everyday language. Some of the words are not decodable, but you can help your child to read them in the context of the story.

- For each story, talk about the title and look through the pictures so that your child can see what each one is about.
- Read the story to your child, placing your finger under each word as you read.
- Read the story again and encourage your child to join in.
- Give lots of praise as your child reads with you.
- Talk about the story and do the fun activities at the end of each story.

Children enjoy re-reading stories and this helps to build their confidence.

After you have read *Creepy-crawly!*, find the fly hidden in every picture.

These stories include these common words:
called   don't   find   looked   out   said   the   was

For more hints and tips on helping your child become a successful and enthusiastic reader look at our website www.oxfordowl.co.uk.

Creepy-crawly!

Wilma had a creepy-crawly.

She put it in the tub.

Wilma called Dad.

"Get it out," said Wilf.

"Eek! No," said Dad.

Wilf called Mum.

"Get it out," said Wilf.

"Eek! No," said Mum.

Wilf called Chip.

"Get it out," said Wilf.

"Yuck! No," said Chip.

Wilma called Biff.

"Get it out," said Wilma.

"Yuck! No," said Biff.

They all called Kipper.

"Get it out," said Wilf.

"Yes!" said Kipper.

Talk about the story

What trick does Wilma play?

What did Kipper do?

What do you think the creepy-crawly looks like?

What tricks have you played?

Spot the pair

Find the two creepy-crawlies that are identical.

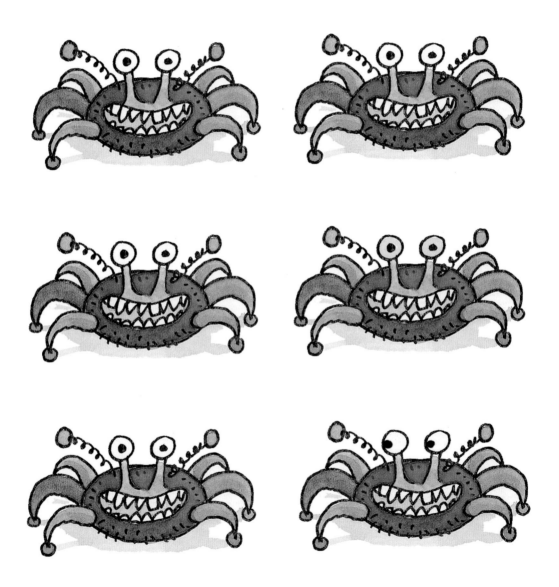

The Lost Puppy

Mrs May had a puppy.

It was called Sniff.

Sniff ran off.

Sniff was lost.

Mrs May was upset.

Biff and Chip looked.

They did not find Sniff.

Wilf and Wilma looked.

They did not find Sniff.

Mum and Dad looked.

They did not find Sniff.

They all looked.

They did not find Sniff.

Floppy looked for his bone.

Sniff was by the tree.

"What a clever dog!"
they all said.

Talk about the story

Why did Sniff run off?

Why was Mrs May upset?

Where did everyone look?

How do you feel if you lose something?

Tangled leads

Who is holding Sniff's lead?

Word search

Find the five words in the grid.

q	a	w	i	n
u	f	i	x	b
q	u	i	c	k
c	u	p	t	c
k	i	s	s	k

cup   fix   kiss

quick   win

Spot the difference

Find the five differences in the two pictures.

READ WITH Biff, Chip & Kipper

The UK's best-selling home reading series

Phonics activities and stories help children practise their sounds and letters, as they learn to do in school.

Stories for Wider Reading have been specially written using everyday language to provide a broader reading experience for your child.

	Phonics	Stories for Wider Reading
Level 1 Getting ready to read		
Level 2 Starting to read		
Level 3 Becoming a reader		
Level 4 Developing as a reader		
Level 5 Building confidence in reading		
Level 6 Reading with confidence		

Read with Biff, Chip and Kipper Collections:

Every collection includes phonics and stories using everyday language

Phonics support

Flashcards are a really fun way to practise phonics and build reading skills. **Age 3+**

My Phonics Kit is designed to support you and your child as you practise phonics together at home. It includes stickers, workbooks, interactive eBooks, support for parents and more! **Age 5+**

Read Write Inc. Phonics: A range of fun rhyming stories to support decoding skills. **Age 4+**

Songbirds Phonics: Lively and engaging phonics stories from former Children's Laureate, Julia Donaldson. **Age 4+**

By the same author

POETRY
The Wind Beyond the Wall.
Story Line Press, Oregon, 1990, reprinted 1991.

A Walled Garden in Moylough.
Story Line Press, Oregon and Salmon Poetry, Co. Clare, 1995.

Winter in the Eye - New and Selected Poems.
Salmon Poetry, Co. Clare, 2003.

AS EDITOR
The White Page - An Bhileog Bhán: Twentieth-Century Irish Women Poets.
Salmon Poetry, Co. Clare, 1999, reprinted 2000, 2001, 2007. (anthology)

The Watchful Heart - A New Generation of Irish Poets - Poems and Essays.
Salmon Poetry, Co. Clare, 2009. (anthology)

CD
The Long Light on the Land - Selected Poems: read to a background
of traditional Irish airs and classical music.
Ernest Lyons Productions, Cloondeash, Castlebar, Co. Mayo, 2004